Lizzy

by Donna Latham
illustrated by Cheryl Mendenhall

Ben's pet lizard
was not in her cage.

"Where is Lizzy?"
asked Ben.

"She must be hiding,"
said Anna.
"Lizzy is good at hiding!"

"Let's look on the couch,"
Anna said.

"I don't see Lizzy
on the couch,"
Ben said.
"Where did she go?"

"Let's look under the rug,"
said Ben.

"Lizzy must be hiding,"
Anna said.
"I don't see her
under the rug!"

"Is Lizzy on the chair?"
asked Anna.

"I don't see Lizzy
on the chair," Ben said.
"Where is she?"

"Let's look on the plant," said Anna.

"Lizzy must be hiding," said Ben.
"I don't see her on the plant."

11

"Is Lizzy on the table?"
Ben asked.

"I don't see her,"
said Anna.

"I have a plan!" said Ben.
"Come with me."

"Hi, Mom," said Ben.
"May I have a strawberry?"

"Yes," said Mom.
"Here is a big strawberry."

Ben put the strawberry
in Lizzy's cage.

"Hi, Lizzy,"
said Ben and Anna.

Fountas & Pinnell

Leveled Literacy Intervention

Fiction

My Take-Home Book

Green System

Book 76

Level E

Heineman

www.heinemann.c

ISBN-13:978-0-325-01891-1
ISBN-10:0-325-01891-X

90000>

9 780325 018911